THIS WALKER BOOK BELONGS TO:

Gillian Rainey

Consultant: Gussie Hearsey
On behalf of the Pre-school Playgroups Association

First published 1988 by Walker Books Ltd
87 Vauxhall Walk, London SE11 5HJ

This edition published 1992

Text © 1988 Walker Books Ltd
Illustrations © 1988 Tony Wells

Printed by Dai Nippon (Hong Kong) Ltd

British Library Cataloguing in Publication Data
A catalogue record for this book is available from the British Library.

ISBN 0-7445-2337-0

NOIsy noiSES
ON THE ROAD

Tony Wells

WALKER BOOKS
LONDON

The horn on the bus went
beep, beep, beep.
The bell on the bus went
ding, ding, ding.

And the bus drove off . . .

The engine of the police car
went rrmm, rrmm, rrmm.
The siren on the police car
went nee-na-nee-na-nee-na.

But the bus didn't stop.

The horn on the lorry
went blaaaaaaaare.
The wheels on the lorry
went screeech.

But the bus didn't stop.

The engine of the motorbike
went brmm, brmm, brmm.
The siren on the helmet
went wheeeeeeee.

But the bus didn't stop.

The engine of the posh car
went purr, purr, purr.
The wipers on the posh car
went swish, swish, swish.

But the bus didn't stop.

The bell on the bicycle
went tingalingaling.
The wheels on the bicycle
went wobble, wobble.

But the bus didn't stop.

The gate on the crossing
went clang, clang.
The whistle on the train
went whoo-ooooo.

And guess what happened?

The bus finally stopped . . .

and the foxes got all the
things they dropped!

MORE WALKER PAPERBACKS
For You to Enjoy

NOISY NOISES ON THE FARM
by Julie Lacome

Animal sounds, colourful pictures and a delightful
conclusion make this a thoroughly enjoyable picture book for young children.

0-7445-2336-2   £2.99

MY LITTLE BOOK OF COLOURS
MY LITTLE BOOK OF NUMBERS
by Jan Ormerod

Getting dressed and having a party are the two activities
in these delightfully simple introductions to the concepts of
colour and number by one of the world's most popular illustrators.

My Little Book of Colours   0-7445-1474-6
My Little Book of Numbers   0-7445-1473-8
£2.50 each

SING A SONG OF SIXPENCE
illustrated by Julie Lacome

Fifteen favourite nursery songs, including Humpty Dumpty,
Baa Baa Black Sheep, Hush-a-bye Baby and Twinkle Twinkle Little Star.

"Satisfyingly firm and rich backgrounds of field or interior, and nice unusual details."
The Junior Bookshelf

0-7445-1719-2   £3.99

**Walker Paperbacks are available from most booksellers, or by post from
Walker Books Ltd, PO Box 11, Falmouth, Cornwall TR10 9EN.**

To order, send: title, author, ISBN number and price for each book ordered, your full name and address
and a cheque or postal order for the total amount, plus postage and packing:

UK and BFPO Customers – £1.00 for first book, plus 50p for the second book and plus 30p for each additional book to a maximum charge of £3.00.
Overseas and Eire Customers – £2.00 for first book, plus £1.00 for the second book and plus 50p per copy for each additional book.
Prices are correct at time of going to press, but are subject to change without notice.